CONTENTS

NAKAMURA LOCK – p. 20

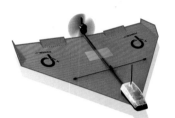

INVADER – p. 22

THERMAL – p. 25

EMPERION ONE – p. 29

ONSLAUGHT – p. 32

VALKYRIE – p. 36

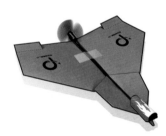

A-9 EAGLE – p. 40

MAESTRO – p. 43

FIRESTRIKE – p. 47

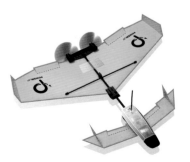

HAMMERHEAD – p. 52

AN INTRODUCTION TO
POWERUP

The *POWERUP Paper Airplane Book* was created as a collaboration between Shai Goitein and Kyle Boyer. Shai is the founder of POWERUP and the inventor who introduced the world to Powered Paper Airplanes. Kyle is a master creator who designs incredible paper airplanes, some of which have featured in national and international competitions. He is also the owner of Foldable Flight, a leader in the space of paper airplane books and video tutorials.

The purpose of this book is to guide the young and old, the newbie and the experienced folder, the STEM teacher and the parent, through the wonder and challenges of Powered Paper Airplanes. In it, you will find content dedicated to three of POWERUP's best selling models — the free flight POWERUP 2.0, the smartphone-controlled POWERUP 3.0, and the twin-motored POWERUP 4.0 with computer-aided performance. We'll guide you through the basics of aerodynamics and how they apply to paper airplanes. We'll also give you a crash course on folding, assembling, adjusting, and flying the 10 designs included in the book. These planes range in folding difficulty from easy to advanced, and each works with multiple POWERUP modules.

SHAI

KYLE

For more amazing paper airplane content from Kyle Boyer, head to **FoldableFlight.com**

FOLDABLE FLIGHT'S **INCREDIBLE PAPER AIRPLANES**
+ video tutorials!

15 STEP-BY-STEP **DESIGNS** with illustrated

"As I now reflect on my creation of the first POWERUP modules, there's one moment that stands out to me most. I remember gasping in awe as I watched my propelled paper airplane defy gravity for the first time. I literally shouted in joy at the triumph! Later that day I thought, 'I can't keep this invention to myself. I must share it with others so that the world can experience the same joy I had in flying these motorized paper airplanes.' In that moment, POWERUP was born."

— Shai Goitein, the inventor and founder of POWERUP

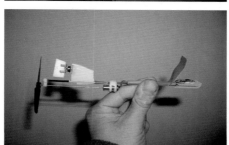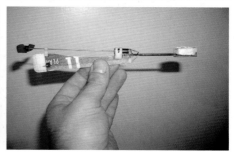

Several prototypes for the first models of POWERUP, which were remote controlled

A STORY OF INVENTION

As a former pilot, I always had a desire to share my love of flight with both children and adults. In 2007, I volunteered to teach aerodynamics to underprivileged kids and, during this time, I began researching new technological advancements in the field of micro flyers. I found that significant advancements had been made in a number of areas — micro motors, lipo batteries, micro controllers, and ultra-light carbon fiber had been developed. As I was reading about these technologies, the eureka moment arrived — it was only natural to apply them to paper airplanes. At the time I had ten years of experience as an industrial designer, and problem solving was a passion of mine, second only to flight. So, with a grin, I accepted the challenge before me and began the process of designing the first POWERUP motors.

After countless prototypes and trial after trial, I was able to develop a design architecture that met my standards for performance. Finally, my module produced highly stable and controlled flight while also being compatible with a wide variety of paper airplanes. Here are a few realizations and considerations that guided me through the design process:

• In order for the plane to remain airborne, thrust needs to be equal to at least half the combined weight of the paper and the module. In order to ascend, it needs even more thrust.

• Without landing gear, every flight ends in some kind of crash. For this reason, the module needs to be highly durable. Several design decisions arose from this consideration, one of which is the propeller placement. Rear propellers are much less likely to be damaged in crashes than those placed at the front of an aircraft.

• Good paper airplanes are already well balanced in terms of their centers of gravity (CG) and centers of pressure (CP). I just needed to design the module such that, when the electronics attach to the plane, the CG would be in the same location or slightly forward, which would provide even better stability.

• Most paper airplanes have a V-shaped fuselage, so I needed to design a clip that could work universally with planes of this shape.

• Rather than complicating the design with moving elevators, it made sense to utilize a predetermined angle of attack, just as traditional paper airplanes do. The user can modify this angle of attack by bending the elevators to the desired position before each flight, but doesn't need to adjust it during flight in order to control altitude. Altitude is instead controlled by throttle. As the user increases thrust, the plane's speed and lift both increase. This causes the plane to climb, while reducing thrust causes it to descend.

• Turning right or left could easily be achieved by adding a small rudder just like the ones used on real airplanes.

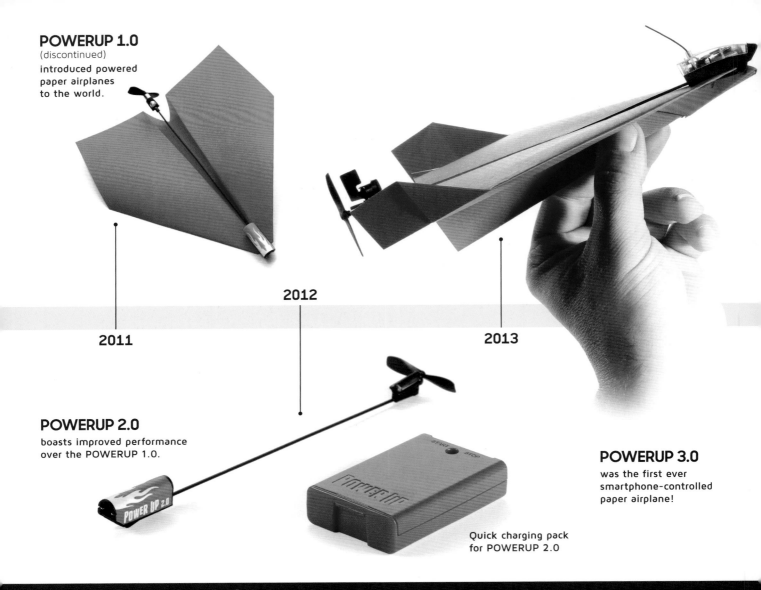

POWERUP 1.0
(discontinued)
introduced powered paper airplanes to the world.

2012

2011

2013

POWERUP 2.0
boasts improved performance over the POWERUP 1.0.

POWERUP 3.0
was the first ever smartphone-controlled paper airplane!

Quick charging pack for POWERUP 2.0

After all of these prototypes, it was again time to put the product to the test. I excitedly drove out to a nearby field where I planned to fly my plane. But, upon my arrival, I realized that in my excitement I had entirely forgotten to bring paper to fold my plane! Desperate, I searched through the glove compartment of my car and found an old, beat up sheet of printed paper. Good enough for me! I eagerly grabbed the paper, folded it, and connected my prototype to the plane. This was the moment of truth. I throttled up and launched the plane into the air. For a moment I worried that it might crash, but no! The flight was a total success!

This flight made it clear to me that my contraption could enable anyone, child or adult, to convert their creations into flying machines. Seeing this potential gave me an intense desire to share my creation with the world. I patented my design and prepared to produce the modules in China.

Even though I had succeeded in creating remote-controlled modules, the first product I released was a simplified model. Possessing an electric motor driven by a super capacitor, the POWERUP 1.0 could make almost any paper airplane ascend, but it wasn't remote controlled. This model (and later the 2.0) would quick charge in 20 seconds and could achieve soaring flights of over 30 seconds. This easily exceeds the world record in time aloft for unpowered paper airplanes.

Following the success of the 1.0 and 2.0, I wanted to take POWERUP to the next level with a mass-manufactured, remote-controlled module. In 2012, while I was exploring various designs for the new model, I met a German start-up company by the name of Tobyrich. They had previously developed a remote-controlled module for foam planes by utilizing bluetooth enabled smartphones. This approach allowed us to use light weight technology similar to the radio-controlled technology I was experimenting with a few years earlier, but this time it could be controlled from a user friendly interface on your phone! At the time, this was extremely innovative — mind blowing, honestly. It was a natural step to integrate the technology into our architecture.

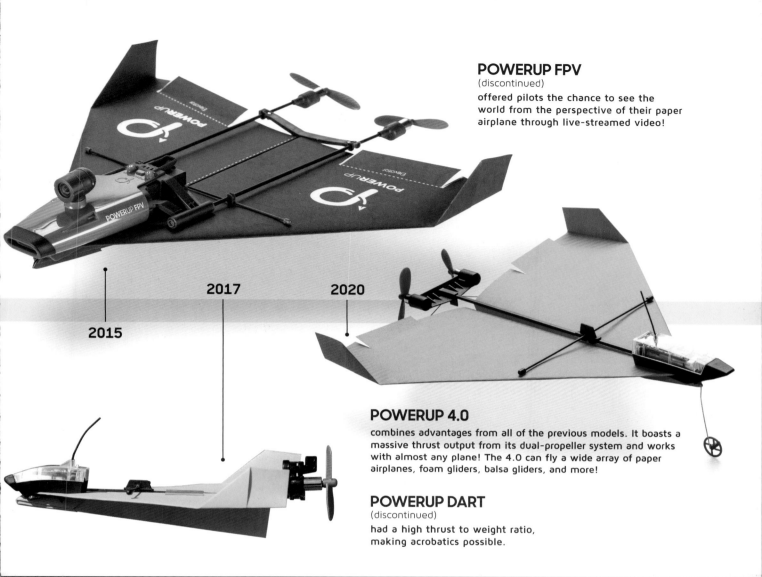

POWERUP FPV
(discontinued)

offered pilots the chance to see the world from the perspective of their paper airplane through live-streamed video!

2015　　　**2017**　　　**2020**

POWERUP 4.0

combines advantages from all of the previous models. It boasts a massive thrust output from its dual-propeller system and works with almost any plane! The 4.0 can fly a wide array of paper airplanes, foam gliders, balsa gliders, and more!

POWERUP DART
(discontinued)

had a high thrust to weight ratio, making acrobatics possible.

The concept was announced at Toy Fair NY in early 2013 and received "the best of toy fair" award by *Popular Science*. Later in 2013, I launched a crowdfunding campaign on Kickstarter for the product now known as the POWERUP 3.0 smartphone-controlled paper airplane. The project launch was explosive and, with our viral video, it reached every corner of the planet, making us the 7th most funded Kickstarter project in the world at the time!

By 2014, drones and first person view (FPV) flying had emerged. As a pilot, I love the bliss of flying high above the earth and experiencing an entirely different and beautiful perspective. I wanted to make it possible for anyone to experience that same view, atop the wings of their own paper airplane. So I collaborated with Parrot, a leader in drone development and video streaming technology. I also collaborated with Zickel Engineering, which specializes in aerospace navigation and control, to develop an autopilot system.

Out of these collaborations arose the POWERUP FPV, which launched on Kickstarter in 2015. The design utilized wifi technology to live stream video from the drone directly to a set of virtual reality goggles, providing a low cost but immersive flying experience. This design was heavier than the 3.0 and required more thrust, so we implemented two powerful motors. The user could easily steer the plane by tilting his or her head to the left or right, up or down. The product received "the gold award for best of innovation" under the drones category at the CES (Consumer Electronics Show) 2016.

Following the creation of the FPV, I was inspired to again approach the technology used in the 3.0. The POWERUP Dart was based on the 3.0, but was designed for paper airplanes half the size, which allowed for reduced weight and drag. This combination opened the door for high-speed flying and aerobatic maneuvering of loops, barrel rolls, and more. The new thrust to weight ratio also made it possible for the Dart to take off from and land on the ground. Over 24,000 backers on Kickstarter made this our biggest project ever, raising over $1.6 million in funding!

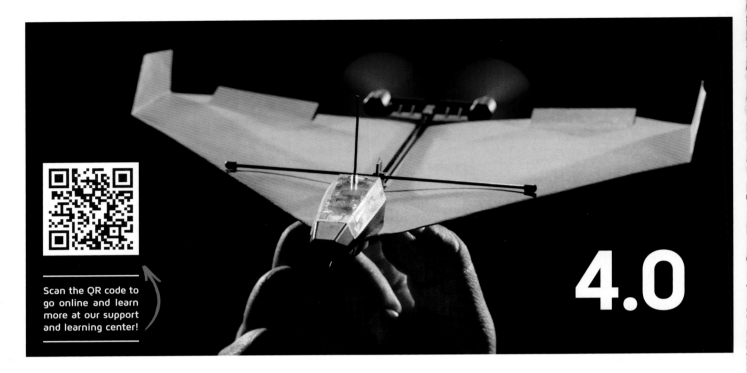

Scan the QR code to go online and learn more at our support and learning center!

4.0

The POWERUP 4.0, our most recent model, integrates key advantages from each of our previous smartphone-controlled modules. We utilized the low cost and easy-to-use bluetooth technology from the POWERUP 3.0 and Dart and meshed it with the twin motor thrust design from the FPV. This auto-stabilized, over-powered design allows for easy control in almost any wind condition and will literally fly almost anything! We're not kidding. We've used lettuce as wings for the 4.0. And, while we don't recommend that you do the same, the 4.0 module is excellent with an extremely wide array of paper airplanes, foam planes, and balsa gliders. The project was launched on Kickstarter in late 2019, and the modules will be delivered to backers in 2020.

POWERUP 4.0 KEY FEATURES

• High thrust output allows the 4.0 to work with many designs, including airplanes constructed from balsa wood and foam.

• Possesses computer assisted stabilization so it can fly almost any paper airplane, even in windy conditions

• Can take off from and land easily on the ground

• Possesses a night flight option with LED's!

• Records flight data and allows you to define unique setting preferences for different planes and flight profiles

• The advanced technology in the POWERUP 4.0 lets you explore designs at an entirely new level, whether you are a beginner pilot or very experienced. We hope you enjoy the ride and create something amazing!

A BIG THANKS!

To my wife and partner who supports me even when I make big mistakes; to my kids who I often dragged along to fly or pose for pictures; to my friends, colleagues, and partners who supported me along the way and put their faith in my crazy ideas; and to all the backers who made these projects possible.

Happy flying,
Shai

What do these symbols mean?

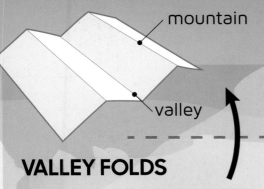

mountain

valley

VALLEY FOLDS

A red dashed line, like the one below, tells you to make a valley fold. The arrow tells you which direction to fold the paper.

You'll come across a bunch of symbols in this book. Each one has a specific meaning for communicating specific folding instructions. Knowing what these symbols mean will help you to successfully fold each plane, so let's take a look at them here:

turn over

90°

rotate

Some symbols are self-explanatory.

MOUNTAIN FOLDS

A red dashed and dotted line tells you to make a mountain fold.

The arrow tells you to fold to the opposite side of the paper. An easy way to do this is to flip the paper over, make the fold, and flip it back over again.

A CLOSER LOOK

The image in the big circle provides a closer look at the portion of the paper in the smaller circle.

EXISTING CREASES

A solid red line highlights a crease you've already made for reference.

FOLD AND UNFOLD

The arrow above tells you to make a fold and then to open that fold back up in preparation for the next step.

1 in = 2.54 cm

In this book, we often provide measurements in both imperial and metric figures. But sometimes there isn't enough space to conveniently do that. We often refer to measurements in inches, so it's well worth knowing how to convert from inches to centimeters.

REFERENCE POINTS

Dots like the one to the left highlight important reference points for folds.

HOW IT WORKS

GET TO KNOW YOUR POWERED PLANES

In this chapter, we won't be explaining traditional flight theory of fixed-wing aircraft. Instead, we'll walk you though a few scenarios that you may encounter as you fly your smartphone-controlled paper airplanes. By understanding what happens in each of these scenarios, you will gain the knowledge necessary to analyze the flights of your planes. But before we begin, let's define a few terms you'll need to know.

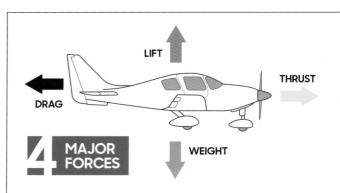

4 MAJOR FORCES

THRUST is the force that propels a plane forward.

DRAG is the friction with air that slows a plane.

WEIGHT is the force that pulls a plane down.

LIFT is the force that keeps the plane aloft.

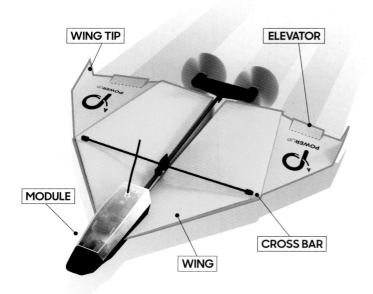

PARTS OF YOUR PLANE

WING TIPS help your plane to fly in a stable manner.

ELEVATORS control the pitch of the plane.

WINGS generate lift to help a plane fly.

WHAT MAKES YOUR POWERUP GO UP?

In our example to the right, the plane, which consists both of the folded paper and the POWERUP 2.0 module, weighs .44 ounces (12.5 grams). In order for our POWERUP paper airplane to ascend, it will need to generate enough lift to overcome its total weight. So how does the plane generate this lifting force? And why does the POWERUP defy gravity in a way that regular paper airplanes can't? To find out, let's take a look at Scenario 1.

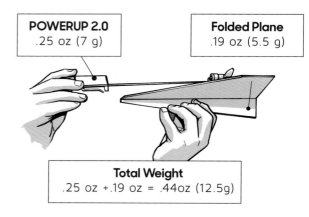

POWERUP 2.0
.25 oz (7 g)

Folded Plane
.19 oz (5.5 g)

Total Weight
.25 oz +.19 oz = .44oz (12.5g)

SCENARIO 1 – LAUNCH

Refer to Figure 1 on the next page. In Step A your propeller is spinning fast as you throttle up and prepare to launch. But, at this stage, your airplane is still in your hand and is not generating any lift. As you move your arm forward and release the plane (Step B), the airplane accelerates due to your throw. The air that passes over and under the wings of your plane will allow them to generate lift and will keep your plane airborne. But this is the point where powered paper airplanes and regular paper airplanes depart in their trajectories! With unpowered planes, drag (the friction between

CONSIDER THIS:

Reducing your paper weight will reduce the overall weight of the assembled airplane.

the aircraft and the air) will slow the plane. As the plane slows, it will generate less lift, and the plane will start gliding down towards the ground (Step D). With powered paper airplanes, the additional thrust generated by the propeller enables the plane to keep accelerating (Step C). As the plane flies faster, it will generate more lift, and it will ascend at a faster rate.

QUESTION:

WHAT HAPPENS WHEN LIFT = WEIGHT?

Your plane will fly at a constant altitude in a level flight path.

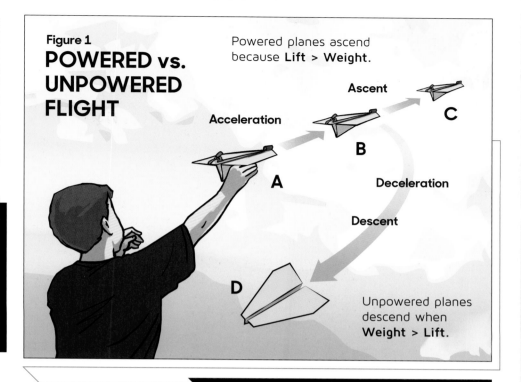

Figure 1
POWERED vs. UNPOWERED FLIGHT

Powered planes ascend because **Lift > Weight**.

Ascent

Acceleration

A

B

C

Deceleration

Descent

D

Unpowered planes descend when **Weight > Lift**.

SCENARIO 2 — NOSE DIVE

This is all nice in theory, but why does my POWERUP paper airplane sometimes nose dive even if it's gaining speed? If we consider the logic laid out in the first scenario, the root cause of a nose dive is reduced lift. So why is the lift reduced in this scenario? Let's take a closer look at other factors that affect the lifting force:

LEARN MORE ABOUT LIFT
Scan the QR code on the left and visit our website to learn more about Bernoulli's law.

ANGLE OF ATTACK (PITCH ANGLE)

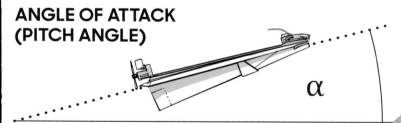

α

Angle of attack, also known as pitch angle, is the angle between the wing and the airflow it meets during flight.

DIRECTION OF AIR FLOW

The higher the pitch angle the more lift the wing generates.
So now we can explain why the plane crashed after take-off. The pitch angle was too shallow. Turn the page to learn how to increase the pitch angle of the plane so it generates more lift.

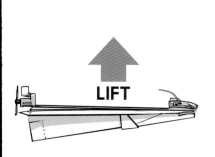
LIFT

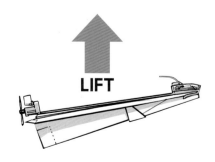
LIFT

LIFT

CENTER OF GRAVITY

The airplane rotates and changes pitch angle around a point called the center of gravity, or CG for short, as shown in Figure 2. The CG is also the point at which gravity, or a plane's weight, pulls the airplane down.

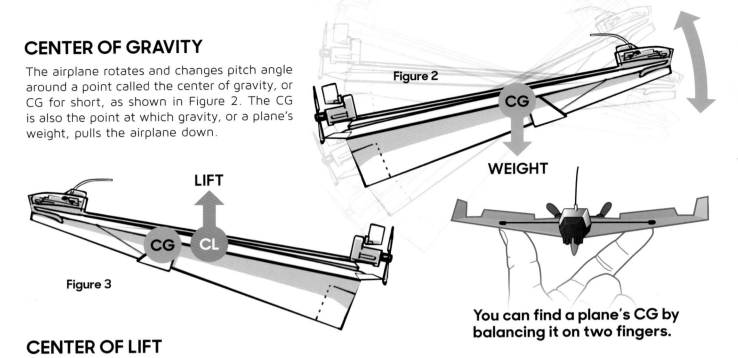

Figure 2

CG

WEIGHT

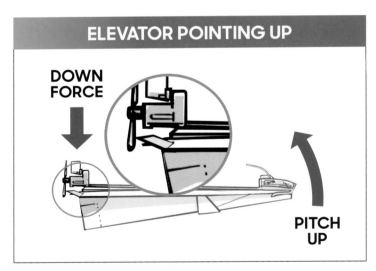

LIFT

CG   CL

Figure 3

You can find a plane's CG by balancing it on two fingers.

CENTER OF LIFT

Similar to the center of gravity is the center of lift, shown in Figure 3, which may be abbreviated as CL. The amount of lift generated in front of the CL is equal to the amount of lift generated behind the CL, and it's the point at which lift acts on the plane to fight gravity. Unlike the center of gravity, the center of lift is not in a fixed position. It depends on flight speed and that plane's angle of attack. You can also effectively move the CL by changing a plane's wing size or shape.

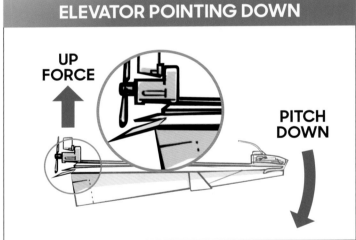

ELEVATOR POINTING UP

DOWN FORCE

PITCH UP

ELEVATOR POINTING DOWN

UP FORCE

PITCH DOWN

The position of the rear elevators will create a force that will either pitch the plane up or pitch the plane down.

Just like in real airplanes, the elevators control the pitch angle of the plane and, in effect, cause the plane to ascend or descend. With paper airplanes the elevator angle is set before takeoff and remains constant throughout flight. This means that the pitch angle of your aircraft is determined even before you launch.

QUESTION:

WHAT ADJUSTMENT IS NEEDED IN ORDER TO ELIMINATE A NOSE DIVE?

Raise your elevator to create a down force at the rear that counterbalances the heavy nose of your plane.

STABILITY IS IMPORTANT!

Understanding the topic of aerodynamic stability is fundamental to understanding the aerodynamics of flying objects. If your paper airplane is unstable, it likely won't be capable of sustaining flight. It will be acrobatic and extremely challenging to control. If it is highly stable, it will fly in a lazy, less maneuverable manner with less potential for acrobatics. This section will help you understand how to fine-tune the stability of your plane.

The stability of an airplane is defined by the manner in which it responds to disturbances in its flight pattern, such as a gust of wind or a temporary maneuver. If, after the disturbance, it has a tendency to return to its original state, then it is said to have positive stability. Most airplanes desire positive stability because it means that they can quickly

THREE KINDS OF STABLE STATES:

Figure 4

A

B

C

Positive Stability (Stable): the marble has a tendency to roll back to its starting position.

Negative Stability (Unstable): any slight movement will cause the marble to change position permanently.

Neutral Stability: the marble does not have a tendency to change position.

and easily recover from temporary changes. Marble A in Figure 4 illustrates this behavior. Even if it is disturbed, it will tend to settle at the bottom of the bowl. Only a major disturbance that throws the marble entirely out of the bowl could prevent it from ultimately returning to its original state.

Marble B illustrates just the opposite. Any small change will cause the marble to roll off the side of the upside-down bowl, and it will not recover to its original state. A paper airplane that stalls and nosedives without control is similar to this marble.

SCENARIO 3 — STALLING

A stall happens when a plane pitches up to an angle that is too steep. As an unstable plane begins to pitch up, the increased angle of attack will also increase lift, and the plane will continue to pitch up. The plane will climb at an ever-steeper angle until it loses speed and airflow detaches from the wings. At this point the plane no longer generates lift and it enters a dive toward the ground. Unstable planes will not be able to recover from a stall.

Stable planes are less likely to stall and are more likely to recover if they do. For a stable airplane, as pitch up occurs, the increased angle of attack will increase lift, but instead of continuing to nose up, the plane will pitch down and return to its original angle of attack and level flight.

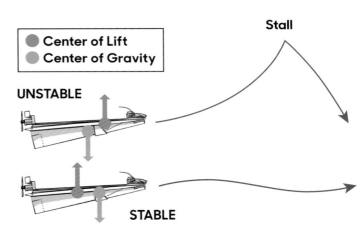

● Center of Lift
● Center of Gravity

UNSTABLE

STABLE

Stall

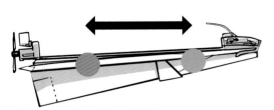

Increasing the distance between the CG and the CL increases stability.

The farther apart the center of lift is from the center of gravity, the more stable the plane will be. The closer the center of lift is to the center of gravity, the less stable and more maneuverable the plane will be.

With POWERUP every plane can be different in shape and design. Each design will have a different flight performance depending on the relationship between the CL and CG locations. If you find that your plane is unstable, you can change that by sliding your module slightly forward. This will move the CG slightly to the front, increasing the distance between the CG and CL, and will make your plane nose heavy and more stable. Of course, like all things in engineering, this is a balancing act. Moving the CG too far forward will cause your plane to dive.

SCENARIO 4 - TURNING

Making your PowerUp plane turn is as simple as leaning your smartphone to one side. But, in order to understand what's really happening when a plane enters a turn, we'll need to discuss a few aerodynamic principles.

First, you'll need to understand two terms: yaw and roll. A plane can rotate on three different axes. The first axis is the pitch axis, which we discuss on the previous page. On this page you can see illustrations for the yaw axis and the roll axis. If a plane is rotating on the yaw axis, it is said to be yawing. If it is rotating on the roll axis, it is said to be rolling. When a plane performs a turning maneuver, it yaws and rolls.

Conventional airplanes use ailerons to control the roll of the plane and rudders to control the yaw. The POWERUP 3.0 uses a rudder to control yaw, while the POWERUP 4.0 uses differential thrust. But, because our paper airplanes don't have controllable ailerons, we can't independently control the roll of our planes.

With that said, we can affect the roll of our planes in an indirect way. Yawing and rolling are related actions such that performing one will cause the other. To understand why that's the case, refer to Figure 5 below to see what happens to a plane that yaws to the right.

Figure 5

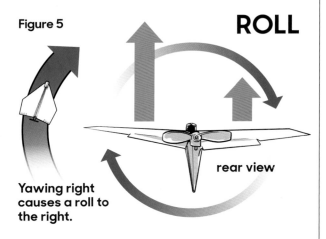

ROLL

rear view

Yawing right causes a roll to the right.

The outer wing moves faster than the inner wing and generates more lift. The difference in lift causes the plane to roll to the right.

As the plane turns to the right, the left wing will move faster than the right wing because it must travel farther in the same amount of time. This will cause the left wing to generate more lift than the right wing, and the plane will roll as a result.

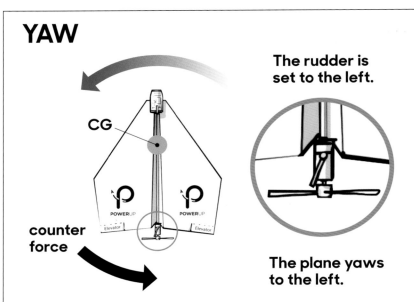

YAW

CG

counter force

The rudder is set to the left.

The plane yaws to the left.

POWERUP 3.0

When a plane yaws, it rotates around its center of gravity. Just as an elevator adjustment can control the pitch of your plane, a rudder can control the yaw. Moving the rudder (highlighted in yellow) to the left will generate a counter force to the right and will cause the entire plane to rotate and yaw to the left. This is how you steer when piloting the POWERUP 3.0.

POWERUP 4.0

The POWERUP 4.0's rear propellers make the plane yaw by generating differential thrust. When the right motor turns faster than the left motor, the airplane will yaw to the left.

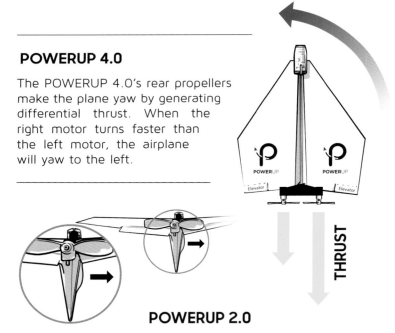

THRUST

POWERUP 2.0

With the POWERUP 2.0, bend the rear of the keel before flight. This bend in the paper (highlighted in yellow) functions like a rudder to achieve the desired left or right turn or to correct an undesired turn. Small adjustments go a long way.

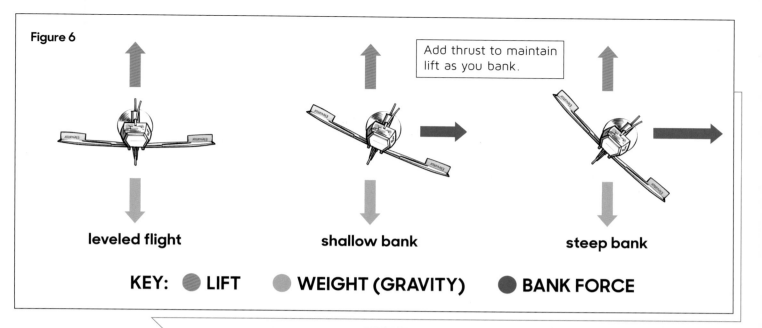

Figure 6

Add thrust to maintain lift as you bank.

leveled flight   shallow bank   steep bank

KEY: ● LIFT   ● WEIGHT (GRAVITY)   ● BANK FORCE

At this point, we've covered how yaw creates a roll action, but now we'll need to discuss how a roll action turns your plane. A plane in leveled flight will maintain its heading thanks to the equilibrium between the lift force and the opposing force of gravity. Lift is always generated perpendicular to the surface of the wings. During a bank the roll angle of the wings will point the lift force into the direction of the bank, creating a bank force as shown in Figure 6. This force will cause the plane to turn in that direction. The steeper the bank, the greater this bank force will be. To keep a leveled flight during a bank, the plane will need to increase the lift force in order to maintain its equilibrium with gravity.

QUESTION:

HOW COULD YOU AVOID LOSING ALTITUDE DURING A TURN?

Increase throttle so that your plane flies faster and generates more lift while in the turn.

Positive dihedral (stable)
rolls a plane back to neutral.

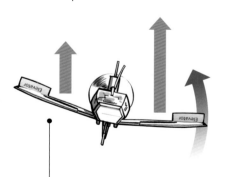

Anhedral (unstable)
rolls a plane into an uncontrolled spiral.

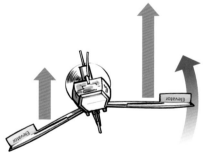

During a roll the lower wing will generate more lift compared to the raised wing, this will cause a restraining effect that will bring the plane to a horizontal stable flight.

STABILITY DURING A BANK

A paper airplane usually performs best when it is designed to self correct in flight. This means that even if it is imperfectly folded, or a small gust of wind knocks the plane off course, it will have a tendency to return to leveled flight. This tendency makes the plane much easier to control.

Wing angle (also known as dihedral) matters greatly when trying to create this kind of stability on the roll axis. Wings that angle up are said to have positive dihedral and will generate positive stability. Wings that angle down are said to have negative dihedral (also known as anhedral). Planes with this wing orientation will be unstable on the roll axis.

1 POWER AND COMMUNICATION CHECK

Check to make sure your PowerUp module is charged. For the 2.0, use fresh alkaline batteries, not rechargeable batteries, in your power pack. For the 3.0 and 4.0, open the PowerUp app on your phone, turn your module on, and hold it near the phone until it connects.

2 CHOOSE YOUR FLYING FIELD

Find a large, grassy field without obstacles such as buildings or trees. Soft ground provides a good landing surface, while asphalt and other hard surfaces may damage your module.

3 WEATHER CHECK

Be sure to also take note of wind speed and direction. If you aren't careful, wind may cause your plane to drift into obstacles at the edge of your fly area. For this reason, you should only fly in winds under 10 miles per hour (roughly 5 meters per second). Check weather apps to confirm wind speed. High humidity can also negatively impact the performance of your plane by affecting the rigidity of the paper. It is best to fly on dry days or with our waterproof templates.

Avoid flying near trees!

10 STEPS FOR SUCCESS

4 CREATE YOUR PLANE

Fold an easy plane from this book for your first flight, and follow the instructions exactly. Use your fingernails to make sharp creases and make all folds symmetrical. Symmetry is crucial to a paper airplane's performance.

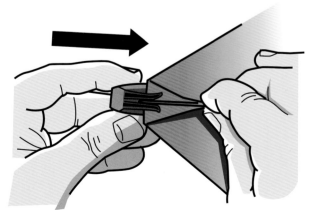

5 ATTACH YOUR MODULE

Insert the front of your paper airplane into the clips of the Smart Module, making sure that the keel goes all the way into the clips. The clips should be on the underside of the plane, and the fin should be between the wings. If the rod of the Smart Module sticks out above the body of the airplane, you can tape the rod to the plane.

60% THROTTLE

Use 60% throttle for your powered test launch and 70 to 75% throttle on your first controlled flight.

6 TRIM (ADJUST) YOUR PLANE

Bend both elevators up slightly. If you bend them too far, they will act as air brakes rather than elevators. Attach the cross bar to the shaft of your Smart Module. This will help hold the wing load and provides a flat dihedral angle for advanced maneuvering. For the 2.0 and 3.0, add a slight right rudder adjustment to the rear of your plane to compensate for the torque of the motor. Read "Scenario 4 — Turning" on page 14 for more information.

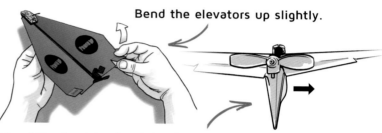

Bend the elevators up slightly.

Bend the keel to the right if you're using the 2.0 or 3.0.

7 TEST LAUNCH WITHOUT POWER

To make sure that your airplane flies well, first test it without providing any thrust from the motor. Launch the plane into the wind and pay attention to whether it glides nicely, dives, or stalls. Make appropriate adjustments (see the Troubleshooting section on page 18) and perform another test launch without power. When the airplane glides steadily, you are ready to fly with the motor running.

8 TEST LAUNCH WITH POWER

Face the wind and choose a distant target to fly to. Double tap the throttle to unlock it and raise the throttle to 60% thrust. Hold your smartphone level so the rudder is in a neutral position, and keep it level for the entire test flight. Launch the airplane with a gentle push. Observe your airplane until it lands. Identify unintended behavior and adjust accordingly. After a successful straight, level flight, you are ready for your first flight with you in command.

9 CONTROLLED FLIGHT

Before taking off, plan your flight path. A good path for beginners is what pilots call the airfield traffic pattern — the path that pilots follow when approaching an airport or taking off from it. This flight path will help you keep the airplane in range during the flight. Set your throttle at 70 to 75% and launch into the wind. The power from the Smart Module's motor controls your airplane's altitude. When the throttle is high, the plane ascends. When the throttle is low or all the way down, the airplane descends (or glides). To turn your airplane, tilt your smartphone gently to the left or right until the airplane is going in the desired direction, and then hold your smartphone level.

Note: The amount of thrust that the airplane needs varies according to the wind conditions and the particular paper airplane that you are using.

AIRFIELD TRAFFIC PATTERN

Downwind Leg

Base Leg

Crosswind Leg

Final

Upwind Leg

10 INSPECT YOUR PLANE

After each landing, check that your module is still correctly connected to your paper airplane. Make small adjustments as necessary to improve flight maneuverability and endurance, and make any needed adjustments to your paper airplane. If your plane is significantly damaged by a crash, it's not hard to make another! Recharge your plane after every flying session and before storage.

TROUBLESHOOTING

WE'RE GOING DOWN!

OBSERVATION ➡ ANALYSIS ➡ ACTION

The first step in troubleshooting is to make an **observation** of your plane in flight and note its behavior. Is it diving? Is it spiraling out of control? Next you'll need to perform an **analysis** to determine why the plane behaves in that manner. Then you'll need to identify a likely cause for the behavior and take corrective **action** as advised below. Once you have made a correction, it's back to the beginning of the process. **Observe**, **analyze**, and take more corrective **action** if necessary.

KEY

Problems you're likely to encounter, even when using planes from this book, are marked with blue icons.

Problems you're less likely to encounter are marked with yellow icons.

Problems you won't encounter unless you're experimenting with planes from outside this book are marked with black icons.

A–Z

Likewise, problems and their solutions are listed alphabetically, with "A" being the most likely.

OBSERVATION: My airplane always dives into the ground at launch.

PRIMARY ANALYSIS: A heavy nose causes the plane to dive.

A **The elevators are not compensating for your plane's tendency to pitch down.**
Raise the elevators slightly to change the pitch of the plane so it flies level.

B **The plane does not have enough airspeed at launch to generate lift.**
Verify that you are launching heading into the wind at 60-80% thrust. Consider increasing thrust even further if problem persists.

C: Slide the module all the way onto the nose of the plane.

C **Your module is not properly attached to the plane.**
Slide the module all the way onto the nose of the plane and verify that the module sits flat on the wing.

D **The center of gravity (CG) is located too far forward on the plane.**
Move the CG by sliding the module all the way onto the nose of your plane if it isn't already in this position. Otherwise, adjust the design of your plane to move the CG to the rear.

E **The center of lift (CL) is located too far towards the rear of the plane.**
Reduce the size of the plane's wings by folding wing tips or by changing the airplane style.

OBSERVATION: My airplane does not climb after take off.

PRIMARY ANALYSIS: The airplane does not fly fast enough to generate lift.

angle of attack

A   **The power level is too low or your batteries are weak.**
Increase the throttle, recharge your module, or replace batteries on your
2.0 power pack. Also be sure to launch the 2.0 immediately after charging.

B   **The plane's angle of attack is too low.**
Raise the elevators slightly or make an adjustment to move the center of gravity to the rear.

C   **The airplane is too heavy.**
Increase wing size to generate more lift, verify that plane is not wet, and/or change to a thinner paper.
20 lb or 80 gsm printer paper is ideal.

D   **The airplane is generating too much drag.**
Verify that your elevators are not bent so far upwards that they are performing as air brakes. Consider
lowering the elevators. Also consider sharpening the creases of your plane to reduce drag.

OBSERVATION: My airplane stalls.

PRIMARY ANALYSIS: The airplane pitches up, loses speed, and then dives.

A   **The elevators are generating too much down force on the rear of the plane.**
Reduce the angle of the elevators slightly.

B   **The center of gravity (CG) is located too far toward the rear of the plane.**
Move the CG forward by sliding the module slightly forward.

C   **Your airplane is flying too quickly.**
If you're flying with the POWERUP 3.0 or 4.0, reduce throttle. If you're flying with the POWERUP 2.0, reduce
the charging time before flight. Also consider reducing your launch speed, especially in windy conditions.

D   **The center of lift (CL) is located too far toward the front of the plane.**
Move the CL towards the rear by increasing the wing surface. Flatten the wing tips or change the plane's design.

**Scan the QR code to learn
more about troubleshooting
on our website!**

OBSERVATION: My airplane constantly banks or rolls into the ground.

PRIMARY ANALYSIS: The airplane is unstable on the roll axis.

A   **The wings of your airplane are not symmetrical or are warped or wrinkled.**
Make a new, cleanly folded, symmetrical plane.

B   **Your airplane does not have a positive dihedral angle to balance unintended roll actions.**
Raise the dihedral of your plane's wings.

C   **The plane's rudder or keel are generating a constant yaw and roll action to one side. This same
affect could be caused by propeller torque.**
Make a slight counter trim correction to the rudder or rear of the keel.

D   **If you're flying with the POWERUP 4.0, your differential thrust setting may be too high.**
Change the banking sensitivity in your app settings.

NAKAMURA LOCK

Speed	**Difficulty**
	EASY
Maneuverability	
	Materials
Endurance	•US Letter or A4 Paper
	•Scissors and Tape

WORKS WITH

2.0 **3.0** **4.0**

ABOUT **THE PLANE**

Designed by Eiji Nakamura, the Nakamura Lock is among the best-known paper airplanes in the world — and for good reason. This plane is easy to fold and flies exceptionally well! If you're looking for a plane to start with, this is the one for you.

SCAN FOR **VIDEO** TUTORIAL

Designed by Eiji Nakamura

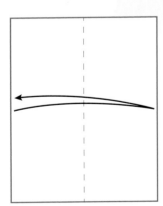

1. Fold the paper in half. Unfold.

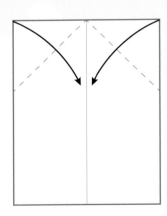

2. Fold the top corners in to the center to form a point.

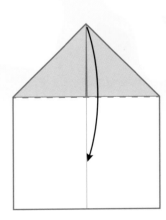

3. Fold the top point down on the indicated line.

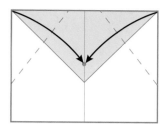

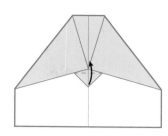

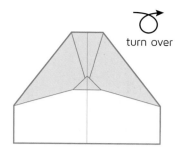

4. Fold the corners to meet at the indicated point, 1 inch above the bottom point of the triangle.

5. Fold the bottom point up on the indicated line.

6. Turn the plane over.

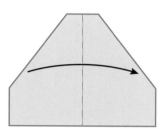

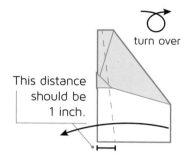

This distance should be 1 inch.

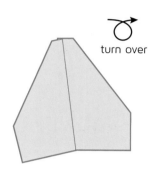

7. Fold the plane in half on the existing center crease.

8. Fold the wing on the indicated line.

9. Turn the plane over.

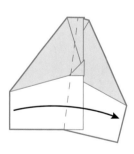

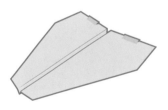

10. Fold the other wing to match.

11. Hold the two wings in alignment and cut the trailing edge of both wings to form the elevators.

12. Open the wings.

13. Finished!

PRO TIP:

When using the POWERUP 2.0, be sure to use alkaline, rather than rechargeable batteries. Don't overcharge the module, and launch the plane immediately after charging. There's no need to discharge the capacitor after each flight — just charge it up again and give it another throw!

Speed

Maneuverability

Endurance

Difficulty
EASY

Materials
•US Letter or A4 Paper
•Scissors and Tape

ABOUT **THE PLANE**

SCAN FOR
VIDEO
TUTORIAL

Invader is one of our
favorite paper airplanes.
Not only is it extremely
easy to fold but, with its
wide wings, it's pretty
easy to pilot as well.
Whether you plan to fly
with the 2.0, the 3.0, or
the 4.0, or even without a
module, Invader is an
excellent choice!

Designed by Shai Goitein

WORKS WITH

2.0   **3.0**   **4.0**

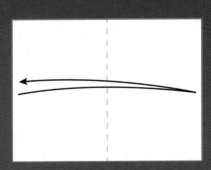

1. Fold the paper in
half. Unfold.

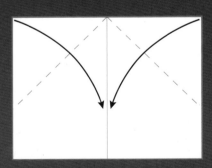

2. Fold the top corners in to
the center to form a point.

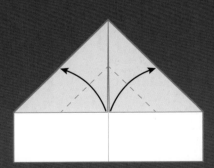

3. Fold the corners on the
indicated 45 degree lines so
each point lands on the edge
of the paper.

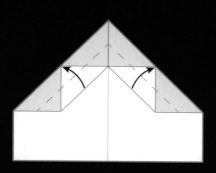

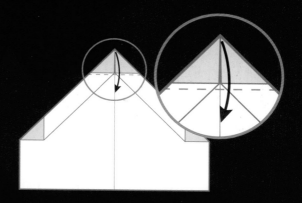

4. Fold the inner diagonal edges of the paper to land on the outer edges of the paper.

5. Fold the top point down on the indicated line. The crease you create should be just below top edges of the top layers of the plane.

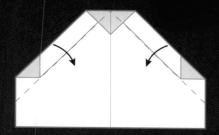

Tape here   and here.

turn over

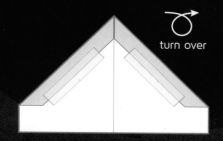

6. Fold the edges of the plane in on the indicated lines.

7. Apply tape in the locations shown.

8. Turn the plane over.

turn over

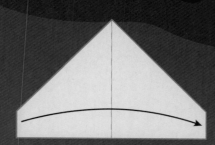

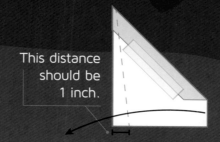

This distance should be 1 inch.

9. Fold the plane in half using the existing center crease.

10. Fold the wing on the indicated line.

11. Turn the plane over.

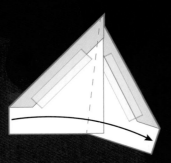

turn over

12. Fold the other wing to match.

13. Fold a small fin at the edge of the wing. Make sure the crease you create runs parallel to the highlighted edge of the plane.

14. Turn the plane over.

18. Finished!

15. Fold the second fin to match the first.

16. Hold the two wings in alignment and cut the trailing edge of both wings to form the elevators.

17. Open the wings.

LIGHT UP THE SKIES!

Use the POWERUP 4.0 Night Flight Kit for stunning visuals and round-the-clock fun! Also be sure to use our Night Flight Waterproof Template to maximize the glow of your plane and protect it from humid or wet conditions.

Available for purchase at PowerUpToys.com

Scan to learn how to connect your Night Flight LEDs to your plane.

THERMAL

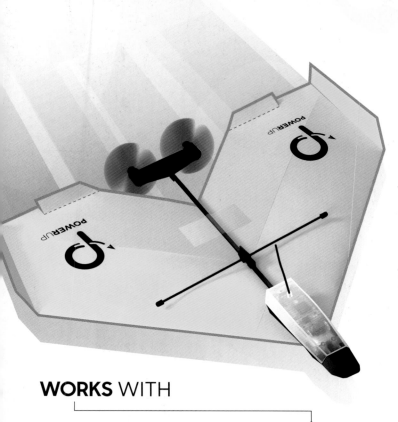

Speed

Maneuverability

Endurance

Difficulty
EASY

Materials
•US Tabloid or A3 Paper
•Ruler, Scissors, and Tape

WORKS WITH

2.0   3.0   **4.0**

Thermal is a beautiful paper airplane with really wide wings, which makes it easy to pilot. It's the perfect plane for the 4.0, but because it is folded from a larger sheet of paper than most planes in this book, it's a little too heavy to fly as well with the 2.0 or 3.0.

Designed by Kyle Boyer

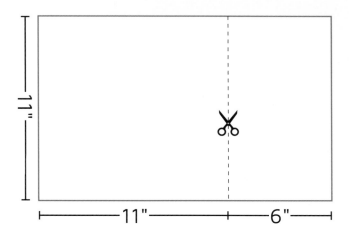

1. Begin by trimming either a US Tabloid (11 x 17 inches) or an A3 sheet to be an 11 x 11 inch square.

2. Fold the square in half diagonally from one corner to the other.

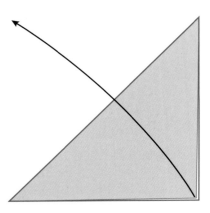

3. Unfold.

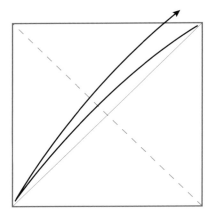

4. Fold the square in half diagonally from one corner to the other. Unfold.

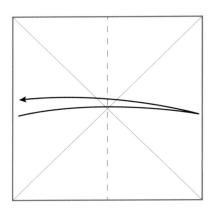

5. Fold the square in half vertically. Unfold.

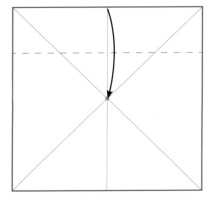

6. Fold the top edge to land on the intersection of the two diagonal creases.

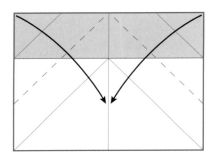

7. Fold the top corners to land on the center crease.

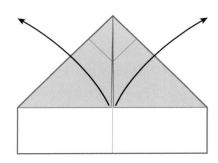

8. Unfold.

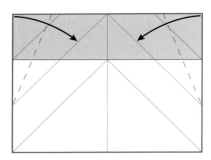

9. Fold the outer edges in to land on the creases formed in Step 7 (highlighted in red).

Tuck these flaps

into this pocket.

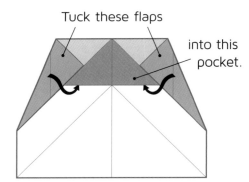

10. Fold the outer edges in using the creases made in Step 7 as your hinge. Tuck the indicated flaps (highlighted in green) into the pocket formed by the central triangle (highlighted in purple).

turn over

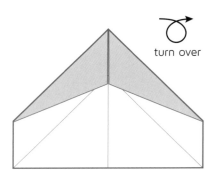

11. Turn the plane over.

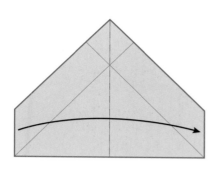

12. Fold the plane in half using its existing center crease.

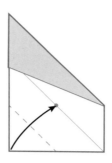

13. Fold the bottom left corner to land on the indicated point. The angle of your crease should be approximately 45 degrees, though anything similar is fine.

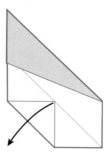

14. Unfold.

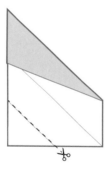

15. Use scissors to cut along the crease made in step 13.

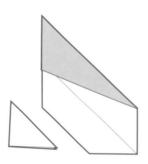

16. Discard the triangular scrap of paper.

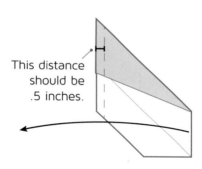

This distance should be .5 inches.

17. Fold the wing on the indicated line.

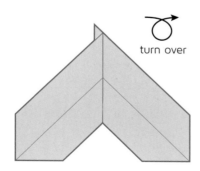

turn over

18. Turn the plane over.

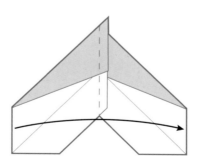

19. Fold the second wing to match the first.

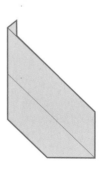

20. Open the wings.

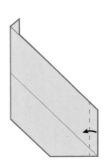

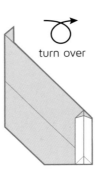

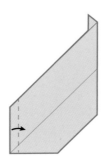

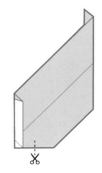

turn over

21. Fold a small fin at the edge of the wing. Make sure the crease you create runs parallel to the highlighted edge of the plane.

22. Turn the plane over.

23. Fold the second fin to match the first.

24. Hold the two wings in alignment and cut the trailing edge of both wings to form the elevators.

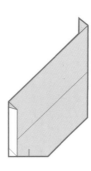

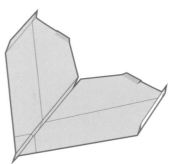

HAMMERHEAD

LOOP

25. Open the wings.

26. Finished!

BARREL ROLL

PRO TIP:

PERFORMING AERIAL MANEUVERS

• Increase throttle as you turn to keep your plane at a constant altitude.

• In order to perform a loop, first gain altitude. Once your plane is high in the air, quickly reduce throttle so the plane enters a dive. Once it's diving, increase throttle to 100%. If you're struggling to perform a loop, land your plane and bend the elevators up slightly.

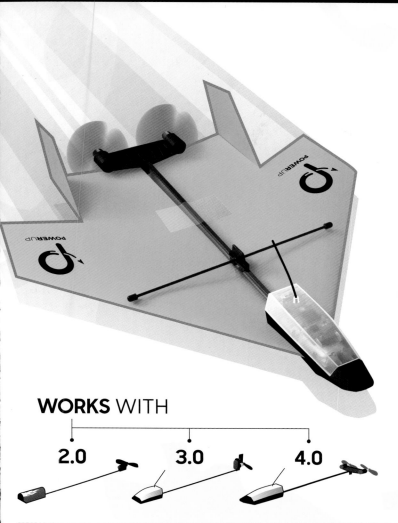

EMPERION ONE

Speed

Maneuverability

Endurance

Difficulty
EASY

Materials
• US Letter Paper (24lb)
• Scissors and Tape

WORKS WITH

2.0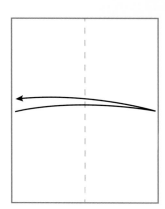

3.0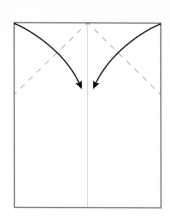

4.0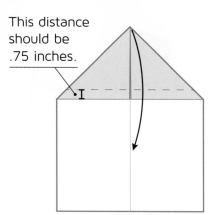

ABOUT **THE PLANE**

Emperion One is, in my own estimation, one of the coolest planes in the book. It looks great, it flies great, it's easy to fold, and it works with the PowerUp 2.0, 3.0, and 4.0. What more can you want from a plane? Fold this one, and you won't be disappointed!

Designed by Kyle Boyer

1. Fold the paper in half. Unfold.

2. Fold the top corners in to the center to form a point.

This distance should be .75 inches.

3. Fold the top point down. The crease you make should be three-quarters of an inch above the bottom edge of the top triangles.

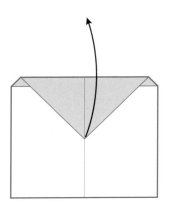

4. Unfold.

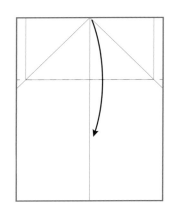

5. Fold the top edge down using the crease made in Step 3. Extend the crease all the way to the edges of the paper.

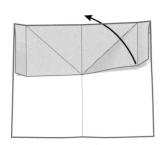

6a. Fold toward the center on the existing diagonal crease, highlighted in red.

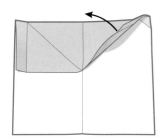

6b. Continue folding along that crease until it lands on the center crease. Notice that the right side of the paper won't lie flat.

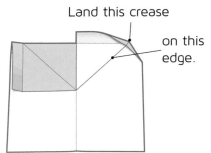

Land this crease on this edge.

6c. Flatten the pocket on the right side to match the illustration in Step 7. Be sure to align the highlighted crease with the diagonal edge of the layer beneath it.

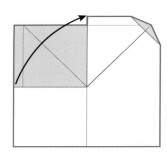

7. Fold the other side to match.

8. Fold the inner corners to land on the horizontal crease as shown.

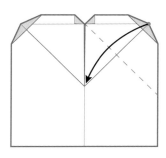

9. Fold the indicated corner to land on the center crease as shown.

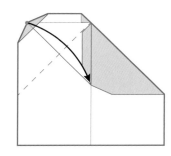

10. Fold the indicated corner to land on the center crease as shown.

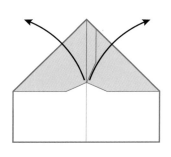

11. Unfold.

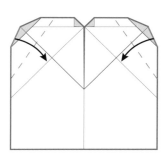

12. Fold the highlighted edges to land on the existing diagonal creases that were created in Steps 9 and 10.

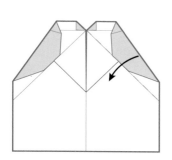

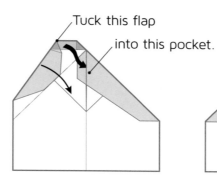

Tuck this flap
into this pocket.

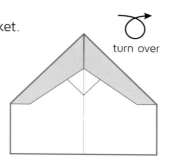

turn over

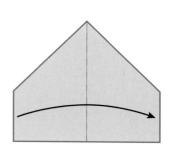

13. Fold the right side in using the highlighted crease.

14. Fold the left side in using the highlighted crease and tuck the left flap into the right pocket.

15. Turn the plane over.

16. Fold the plane in half using the existing center crease.

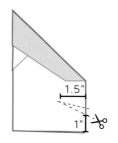

1.5"

1"

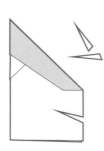

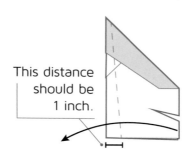

This distance should be 1 inch.

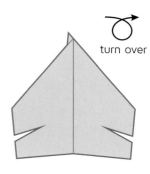

turn over

17. Use scissors to cut small triangles out of the wings as shown.

18. Discard the scraps of paper.

19. Fold the wing on the indicated line.

20. Turn the plane over.

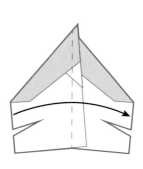

turn over

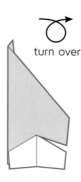

21. Fold the other wing to match the first.

22. Fold the fin on the indicated line. Make sure your crease is parallel to the highlighted edge of the plane.

23. Turn the plane over.

24. Fold the second fin to match the first.

25. Unfold both fins.

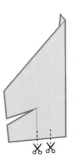

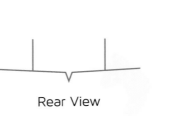

Rear View

26. Hold the two wings in alignment and cut the trailing edge of both wings to form the elevators.

27. Open the wings and set them to match the orientation shown in the rear view.

28. Finished!

ONSLAUGHT

Speed

Maneuverability

Endurance

Difficulty
INTERMEDIATE

Materials
• US Letter or A4 paper
• Scissors and Tape

ABOUT **THE PLANE**

Onslaught is great at many things, but it's truly your best choice for use with the PowerUp landing gear. Nothing is quite as satisfying as bringing your plane in for the perfect landing after an epic flight. Give it a fold and put your piloting skills to the test!

SCAN FOR **VIDEO** TUTORIAL

WORKS WITH

2.0   3.0   4.0

Designed by Kyle Boyer

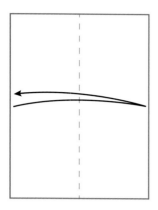

1. Fold the paper in half. Unfold.

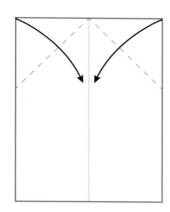

2. Fold the top corners in to the center to form a point.

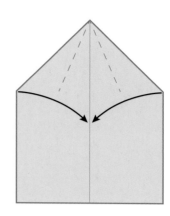

turn over

3. Turn the paper over.

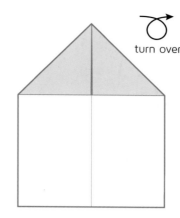

4. Fold the diagonal edges to meet in the center, but only crease where highlighted in red in Step 5.

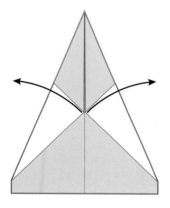

5. Crease on the highlighted portions of the leading edges of the plane. Unfold to match the illustration in Step 6.

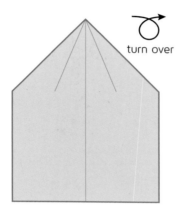

turn over

6. Turn the paper over.

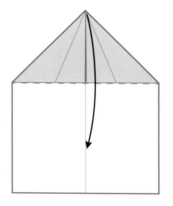

7. Fold the top point down on the indicated line.

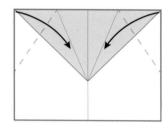

8. Fold the corners in to land on the highlighted diagonal creases.

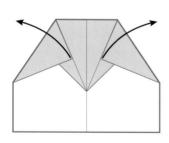

9. Unfold.

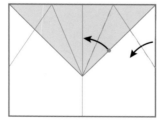

10a. Grab the paper at the highlighted point and swing that edge to land on the center crease. The paper will fold on both diagonal creases, as shown. Refer to Steps 10b through 10d to see this in process.

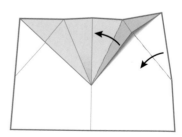

10b. Continue swinging the edge in. The paper should be folding on both highlighted creases.

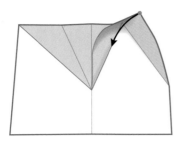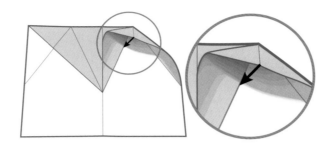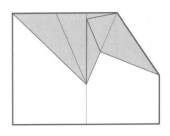

10c. Once the highlighted edge lands on the center crease, begin to pull the indicated corner down.

10d. Land the highlighted crease on the highlighted edge and flatten the paper. Refer to the illustration in Step 11 to see what your model should look like.

11. Repeat Steps 10a through 10d on the left side.

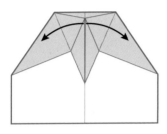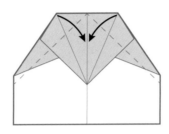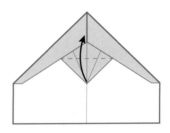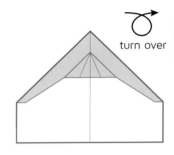

turn over

12. Fold the top flaps on the existing diagonal creases to match the illustration in Step 13.

13. Fold the top corners in to the center.

14. Fold the bottom point up on the indicated line.

15. Turn the plane over.

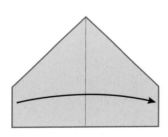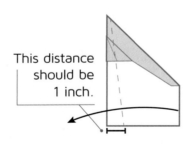

This distance should be 1 inch.

17. Fold the wing along the indicated line.

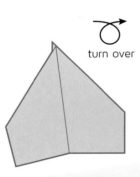

turn over

16. Fold the plane in half using the existing center crease.

18. Turn the plane over.

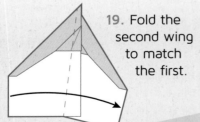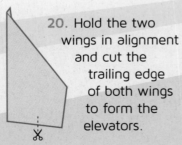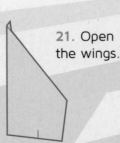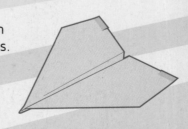

19. Fold the second wing to match the first.

20. Hold the two wings in alignment and cut the trailing edge of both wings to form the elevators.

21. Open the wings.

22. Finished!

1

Place the rear wheels in the orientation shown and slide them into the rear clip until you hear a click.

2

Slide the front wheel into the front clip as shown.

3 Make sure the nose of your plane sits higher off the ground than the tail. This gives the plane a good angle of attack for taking off.

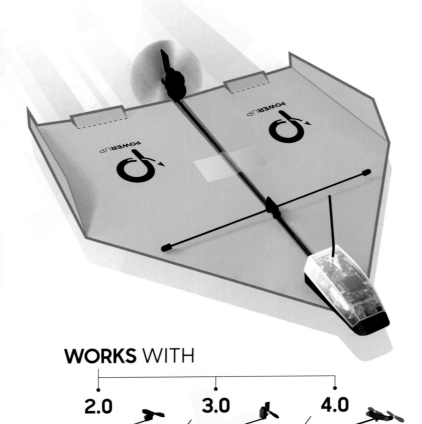

VALKYRIE

Speed	**Difficulty**
Maneuverability	**INTERMEDIATE**
Endurance	**Materials**
	•US Letter Paper
	•Scissors and Tape

ABOUT **THE PLANE**

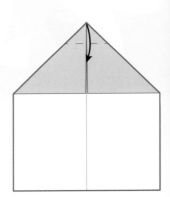

SCAN FOR VIDEO TUTORIAL

Valkyrie is a simple-looking paper airplane, but it uses a clever folding sequence to lock its layers together in an aerodynamic fashion. It also has a large wing area, which makes it a plane perfect for slow and graceful flights that seem to never end.

Designed by Kyle Boyer

WORKS WITH

2.0   **3.0**   **4.0**

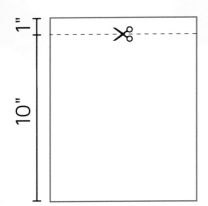

1. Measure and cut the top inch off of the paper so that your resulting rectangle is 8.5 by 10 inches.

1"
10"

2. Fold the paper in half. Unfold.

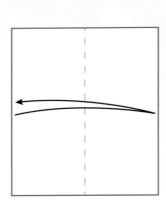

3. Fold the top corners in to the center to form a point.

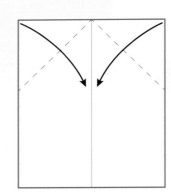

4. Fold the top point down about 1 1/4 inches from the top.

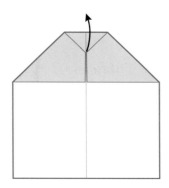

5. Unfold.

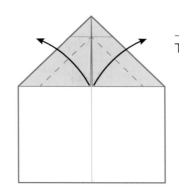

6. Fold the highlighted edges so that they land on the crease made in Step 4.

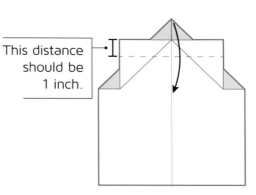

This distance should be 1 inch.

7. Fold the top section down as shown.

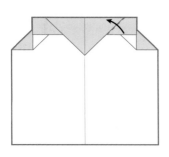

8a. Follow Steps 8b through 8d to perform a swivel fold.

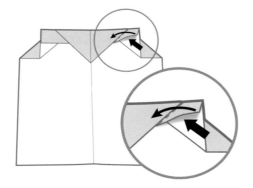

8b. Pull open the pocket and fold along the edge of the triangular top layer. The pocket will not lie flat.

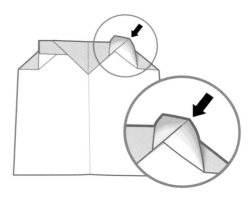

8c. Begin pushing down on the open pocket.

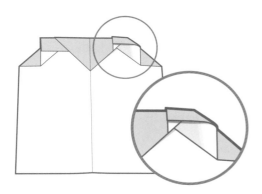

8d. Flatten the pocket to match the illustration in Step 9.

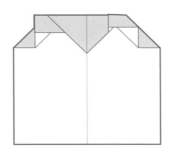

9. Repeat Steps 8a through 8d on the left side.

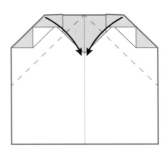

10. Fold the top corners in to land on the center crease.

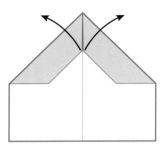

11. Unfold.

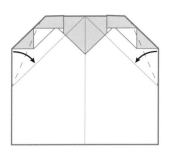

12. Fold the outer edges in to land on the creases made in Step 10.

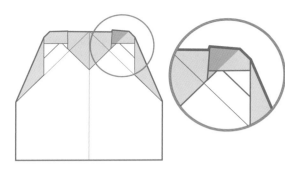

13. Notice that the triangular section highlighted in green is a flap. You're going to use that flap in the next step.

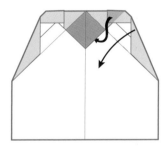

14. Fold in using the existing diagonal crease. As you do so, tuck the flap behind the layer highlighted in purple. This will lock the layers together.

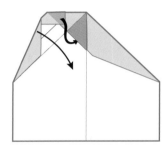

15. Repeat Step 14 on the left side.

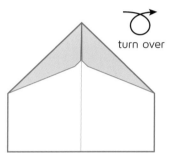

turn over

16. Turn the plane over.

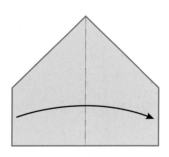

17. Fold the plane in half using the existing center crease.

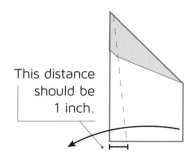

This distance should be 1 inch.

18. Fold the wing on the indicated line.

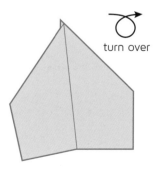

turn over

19. Turn the plane over.

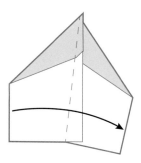

20. Fold the other wing to match the first.

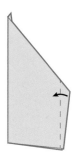

21. Fold a fin on the indicated line. Make sure your crease is parallel to the highlighted edge.

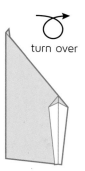

turn over

22. Turn the plane over.

23. Fold the other fin to match the first.

23. Hold the two wings in alignment and cut the trailing edge of both wings to form the elevators.

24. Open the wings.

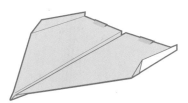

25. Finished!

PRO TIP: INCREASE YOUR FLIGHT RANGE

Increase the flying range of your POWERUP 3.0 or 4.0 by following these tips:

• Straighten the antenna of your module so it stands vertically.

• Hold your phone in portrait (rather than landscape) mode.

• Remove your phone from its case when flying.

A-9 EAGLE

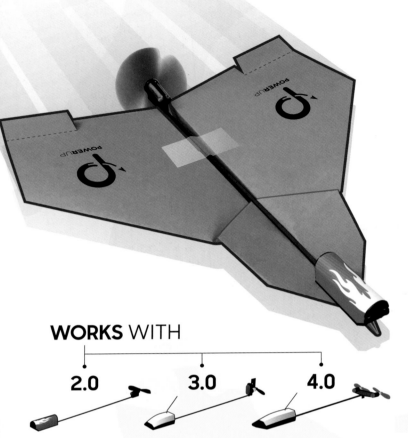

Speed
Maneuverability
Endurance

Difficulty
INTERMEDIATE

Materials
• US Letter or A4 Paper
• Scissors and Tape

WORKS WITH

2.0   **3.0**   **4.0**

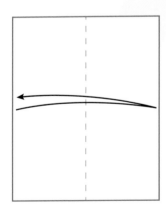

1. Fold the paper in half. Unfold.

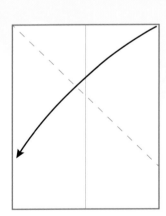

2. Fold the top right corner so that the top edge of the paper lines up with the left edge of the paper. Your crease should go through the top left corner.

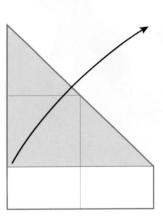

3. Unfold.

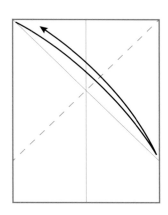

4. Repeat Steps 2 and 3 on the left side.

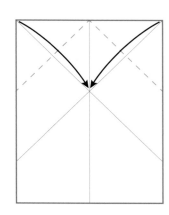

5. Fold the top corners in to the center, but leave a slight gap as shown by the illustration in Step 6.

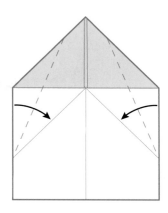

6. Fold the outer edges in to land on the diagonal creases.

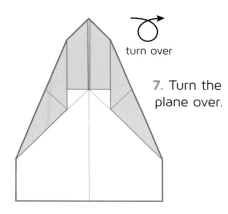

turn over

7. Turn the plane over.

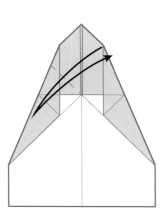

8. Fold the top point down. Make your new crease through the intersection of the existing diagonal creases.

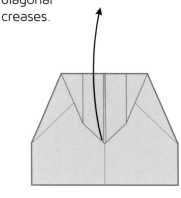

9. Unfold.

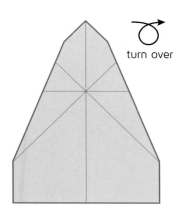

turn over

10. Turn the plane over.

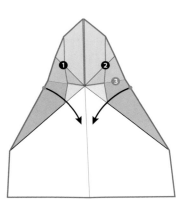

11. Fold along the existing diagonal crease. Unfold. Do both sides.

12a. Grab the paper at the indicated points and pull the outer edges in. The paper should begin collapsing on the bottom half of creases 1 and 2. The left side and right side of crease 3 should both land on the center crease.

12b. A portion of the paper should be standing vertically. Pull that portion of the paper down. It should begin to flatten out.

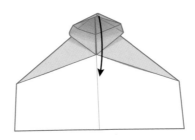

12c. Continue to pull that point down and flatten it to match the illustration in Step 13.

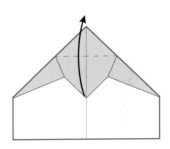

13. Fold the point up on the indicated line.

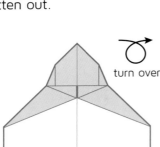

14. Turn the plane over.

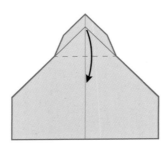

15. Fold the top flap down on the indicated line. This will take some effort, given that the layers are quite thick here.

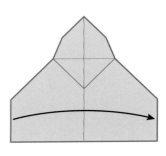

16. Fold the plane in half using its existing center crease.

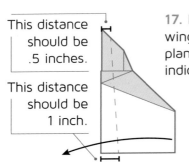

This distance should be .5 inches.

This distance should be 1 inch.

17. Fold the wing of the plane along the indicated line.

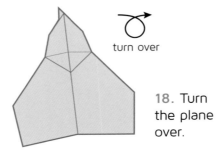

18. Turn the plane over.

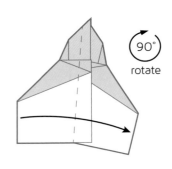

19. Fold the other wing to match. Rotate 90 degrees clockwise.

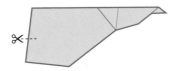

20. Hold the two wings in alignment and cut the trailing edge of both wings to form the elevators.

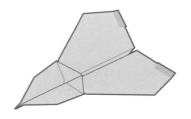

21. Open up the wings.

22. Finished!

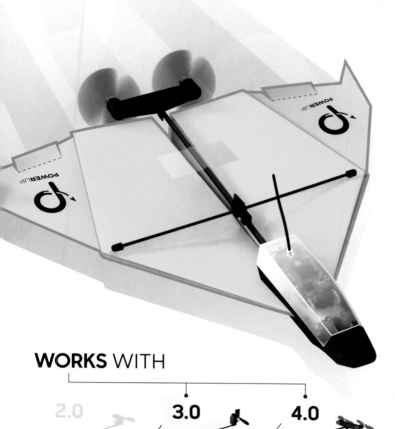

MAESTRO

Speed

Maneuverability

Endurance

Difficulty
INTERMEDIATE

Materials
- US Tabloid or A3 Paper
- Ruler, Scissors, and Tape

ABOUT **THE PLANE**

SCAN FOR
VIDEO
TUTORIAL

Maestro is a beautiful paper airplane that you can fold from any square sheet of paper. That said, in order for it to work with your PowerUp modules, you'll want to fold it from an 11 x 11 inch square. Just cut a US Tabloid or A3 sheet of paper to size and you're good to go!

Designed by Kyle Boyer

WORKS WITH

2.0   3.0   4.0

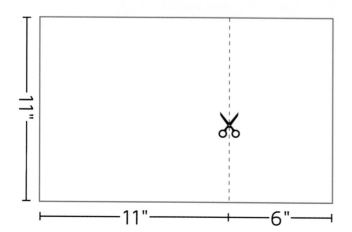

1. Begin by trimming either a US Tabloid (11 x 17 inches) or an A3 sheet to be an 11 x 11 inch square.

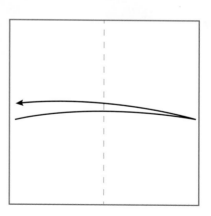

2. Fold the paper in half. Unfold.

turn over

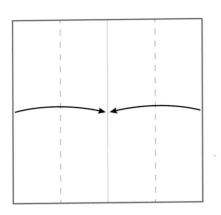

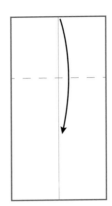

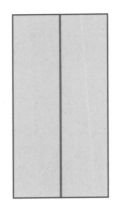

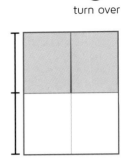

turn over

3. Fold the left and right edges to land on the center crease.

4. Turn the paper over.

5. Fold the top third of the paper down to match the illustration in Step 6.

6. The folded portion should be the same height as the unfolded portion. Turn the paper over.

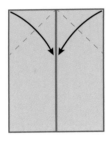

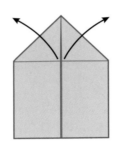

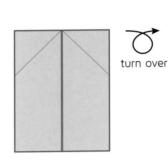

turn over

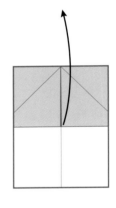

7. Fold the top corners to land on the center crease.

8. Unfold.

9. Turn the paper over.

10. Unfold.

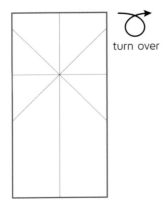

turn over

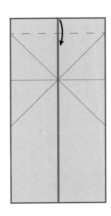

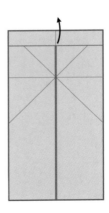

11. Turn the paper back over.

12. Fold the top edge down on the indicated line.

13. Unfold.

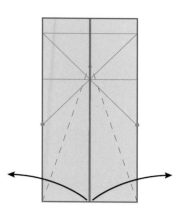

14. Fold on the indicated lines. Each crease should pass through a bottom corner of the paper and the edges should land on the highlighted points as illustrated in Step 15.

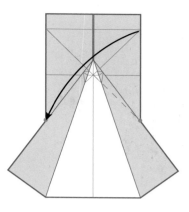

15. Fold along the existing diagonal crease.

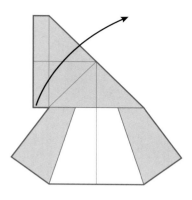

16. Unfold.

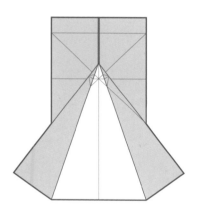

17. Repeat Steps 15 and 16 on the left side.

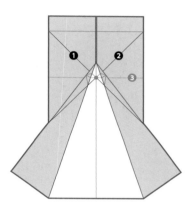

18. Creases 1 and 2 should be valley creases. Crease 3 should be a mountain crease. Poke the intersection marked by the red dot.

19a. Grab the paper at the indicated points and pull the outer edges in. The paper should begin collapsing on the bottom half of creases 1 and 2. The left side and right side of crease 3 should both land on the center crease.

19b. A portion of the paper should be standing vertically. Pull that portion of the paper down. It should begin to flatten out.

19c. Continue to pull that point down and flatten it to match the illustration in Step 20.

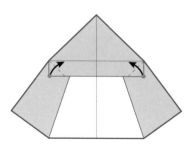

20. Fold the indicated corners in to land on the horizontal crease.

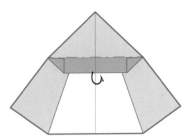

21. Mountain fold the section highlighted in green along the existing horizontal crease. Tuck it behind all other layers to lock the layers together.

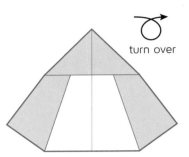

22. Turn the plane over.

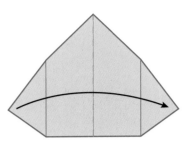

23. Fold the plane in half using its existing center crease.

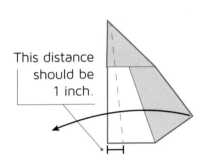

This distance should be 1 inch.

24. Fold the wing on the indicated line.

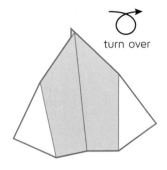

25. Turn the plane over.

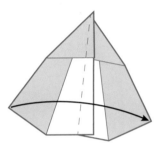

26. Fold the other wing to match the first.

27. Fold a fin on the indicated line. Make sure your crease is parallel to the highlighted edge.

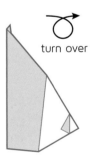

28. Turn the plane over.

29. Fold the other fin to match the first.

30. Hold the two wings in alignment and cut the trailing edge of both wings to form the elevators.

31. Open the wings.

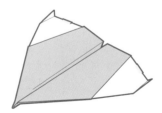

32. Finished!

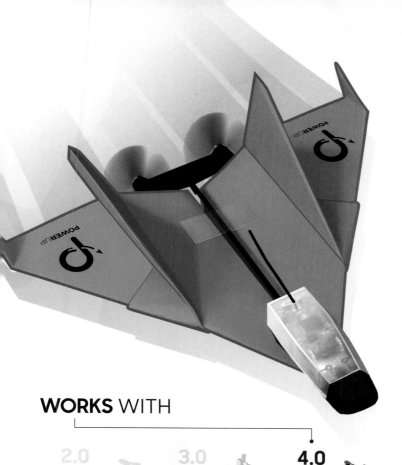

FIRESTRIKE

Speed	**Difficulty**
	ADVANCED
Maneuverability	
	Materials
Endurance	•US Tabloid or A3 Paper
	•Ruler, Scissors, and Tape

ABOUT **THE PLANE**

Firestrike might be the most difficult plane in this book, but it's well worth the effort to fold. Just look at those fins! You'll need a large sheet of paper to fold Firestrike, but don't worry, you can find US Tabloid or A3 paper at your local office supply store.

SCAN FOR **VIDEO** TUTORIAL

Designed by Kyle Boyer

WORKS WITH

2.0   3.0   **4.0**

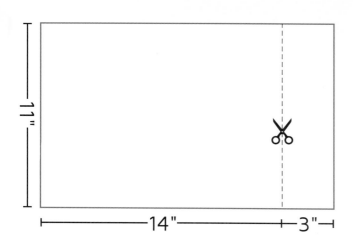

1. Begin by trimming either a US Tabloid (11 x 17 inches) or an A3 sheet to be 11 x 14 inches.

14" 3" 11"

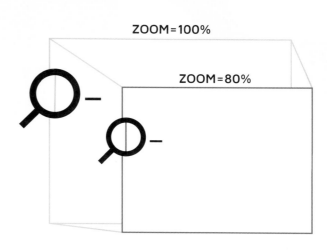

ZOOM=100%

ZOOM=80%

2. Let's zoom out slightly.

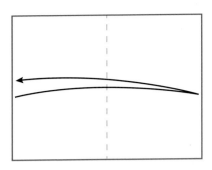

3. Fold the paper in half. Unfold.

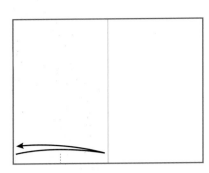

4a. Fold the left edge to center, but don't crease the full length of the paper. Just pinch the paper to form a crease at the bottom edge. Refer to the illustration in Step 4b to see this in process.

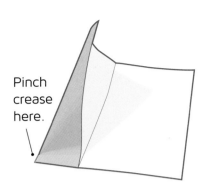

4b. Crease only the highlighted portion of the left edge and unfold.

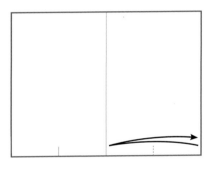

5. Repeat Steps 4a and 4b on the right side.

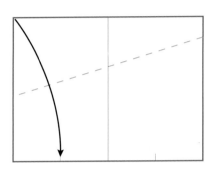

6. Fold the top left corner to land on the left pinch crease formed in Step 4.

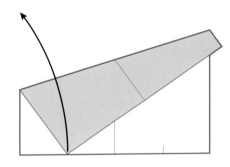

7. Unfold.

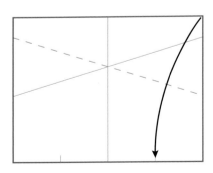

8. Fold the top right corner to land on the right pinch crease formed in Step 4.

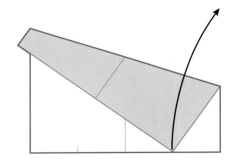

9. Unfold.

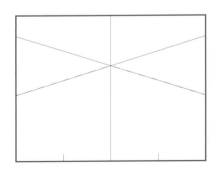

10a. Using the bottom diagonal creases, follow Steps 10b through 10d to Rabbit Ear fold the paper.

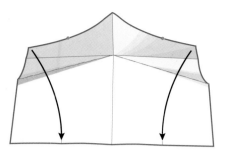

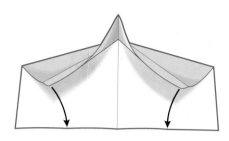

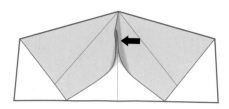

10b. Grab the paper near the highlighted points. Pull the edges in simultaneously, using the bottom diagonal creases as your hinges. Aim to land the corners on the pinch creases made in Steps 4 and 5.

10c. Continue to pull edges in, aiming to land the corners on the pinch creases made in Steps 4 and 5.

10d. Push the central peak to the left and flatten to match the illustration in Step 11.

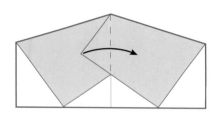

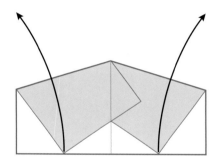

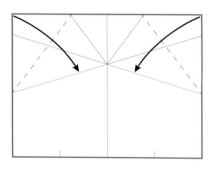

11. Fold the rabbit ear to the right across the center line of the plane.

12. Unfold.

13. Fold the edges in to land on the indicated creases.

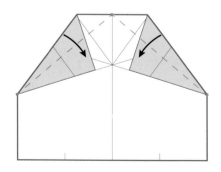

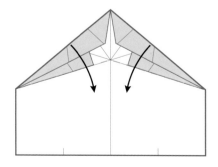

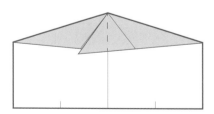

14. Fold from the top point to the indicated point on each side.

15. Perform a rabbit ear fold, as you did in Steps 10a through 10d to match the illustration in Step 16a.

16a. Stand the rabbit ear vertically and follow Steps 16b and 16c to squash fold it.

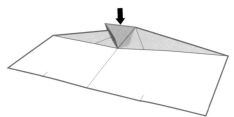

16b. Push down on the spine of the pocket (highlighted in red). The pocket should begin to flatten out.

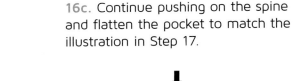

16c. Continue pushing on the spine and flatten the pocket to match the illustration in Step 17.

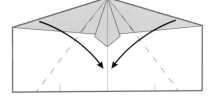

17. Fold the edges in to land on the center crease.

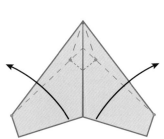

18. Fold the top layer on the indicated lines. Each crease should pass through an outer corner of the plane, and the corner of the underneath layer (shown with blue, dotted x-ray lines).

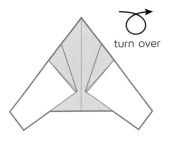

19. Pull the underneath layer out to become the top layer.

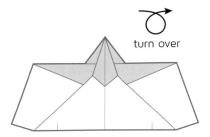

20. Turn the plane over.

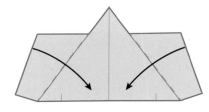

21. Fold each side in along the edges of the top layer.

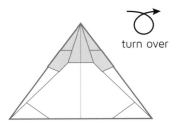

22. Turn the plane over.

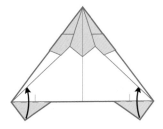

23. Fold the bottom flaps up along the bottom edge as shown. Tuck the flaps under the leading edge of each wing.

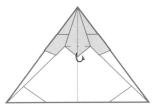

24. Mountain fold the top layer as shown and tuck it behind all of the other layers to lock the layers together.

25. Turn the plane over.

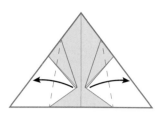

26. Fold the fins on the indicated lines.

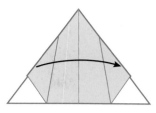

27. Fold the plane in half using its existing center crease.

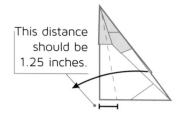

This distance should be 1.25 inches.

28. Fold a wing on the indicated line.

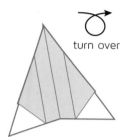

turn over

29. Turn the plane over.

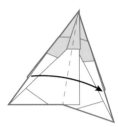

30. Fold the other wing to match the first.

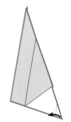

31. Fold a small fin parallel to the highlighted edge of the plane.

turn over

32. Turn the plane over.

33. Fold a small fin to match the first.

Rear View

34. Open the wings and set them to match the rear view shown.

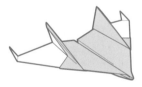

35. Finished!

PRO TIP:

REVERSE CONTROL

It can be a little counterintuitive when you're trying to pilot a plane that is flying towards you. It's like looking in the mirror and all your movements are reversed! In order to make the plane turn left from your perspective, you'll need to tilt your phone to the right. In order to make the plane turn right from your perspective, tilt the phone to the left. If you want it to fly straight, tilt your phone toward the lower wing as shown to the right, and your plane will rock back to a neutral position.

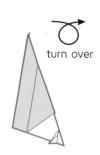

HAMMERHEAD

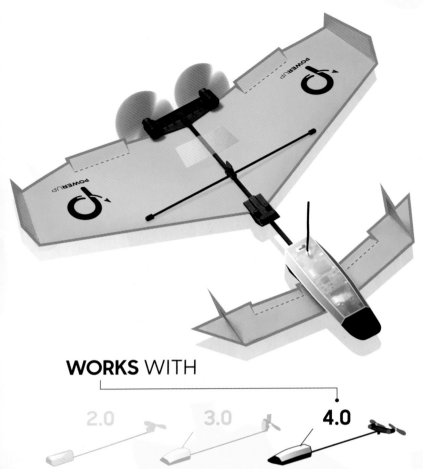

Speed	**Difficulty**
▬▬▬▬▬▬	**ADVANCED**
Maneuverability	Materials
▬▬▬▬▬▬▬	•US Letter or A4 Paper
Endurance	•Scissors and Tape
▬▬▬▬▬	•DIY Bundle

WORKS WITH

2.0   3.0   **4.0**

SCAN FOR
VIDEO
TUTORIAL

ABOUT **THE PLANE**

Hammerhead is an extremely unique paper airplane that utilizes canards (small wings ahead of the main wing) to increase its stability and stall resistance. The front wing and main wing connect to the PowerUp 4.0 separately, so you'll need the DIY bundle for this plane.

Designed by Kyle Boyer and Shai Goitein

Available for purchase at PowerUpToys.com/shop

DIY
BUNDLE

You'll need the DIY bundle in order to properly attach Hammerhead to your PowerUp 4.0 Module.

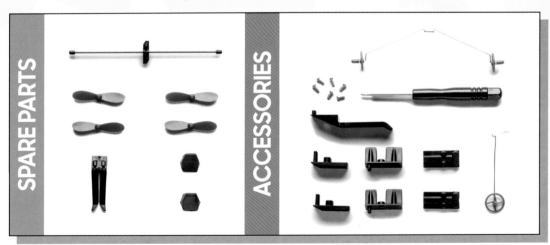

SPARE PARTS

ACCESSORIES

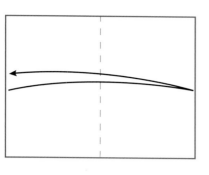

1. Fold the paper in half. Unfold.

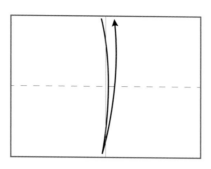

2. Fold the paper in half the other way. Unfold.

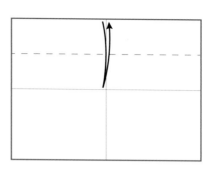

3. Fold the top edge down to land on the crease made in Step 2. Unfold.

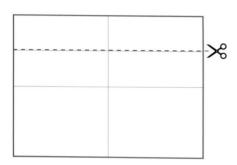

4. Cut the paper along the crease made in Step 3.

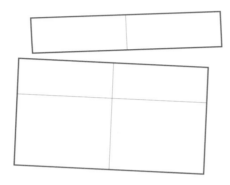

5. Set the larger portion of the paper aside. We'll be using that later.

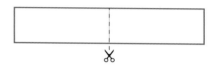

6. Cut the small strip of paper in half along the existing crease.

7. Discard one of the small rectangles (or save it in case you make a mistake while folding the other).

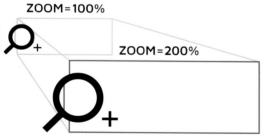

8. Let's zoom in on the small rectangle. Use this sheet to fold the front wing.

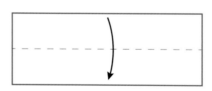

9. Fold the rectangle in half.

10. Fold the top corners so that they land on the bottom edge.

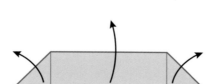

11. Unfold.

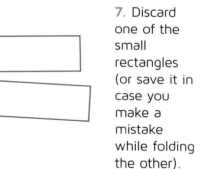

12a. Fold the top edge to the bottom edge, while pushing the edges inward.

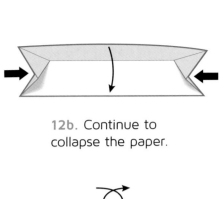

12b. Continue to collapse the paper.

12c. Flatten the paper to match the illustration in Step 13.

13. Fold the top quarter inch of the paper down.

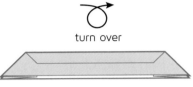

14. Turn the paper over.

15. Fold the paper in half.

16. Fold the wing along the indicated line.

17. Turn the paper over.

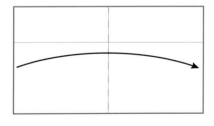

18. Fold the other wing to match.

19. Hold the two wings in alignment and cut the trailing edge of both wings to form the elevators.

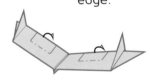

20. Fold the top flap to form a fin. Your crease should run parallel to the highlighted edge.

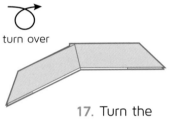

21. Turn the paper over.

22. Fold the top flap to form a fin that matches the first fin.

23. Open the wings.

24. Fold the elevators **down** slightly. These **perform differently** than most elevators because they will be in front of the plane's center of gravity.

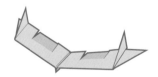

25. You've finished folding the front wing! Move on to Step 26 to fold the main wing.

26. Grab the larger portion of the paper that you set aside earlier. Use this sheet to fold the main wing. Fold the paper in half using the existing center crease.

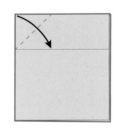

27. Make sure your left edge is your folded edge. Fold the top left corner to land on the horizontal crease.

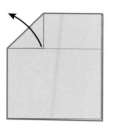

28. Unfold.

29. Stand the section highlighted in green vertically and follow Steps 30a and 30b to perform a squash fold.

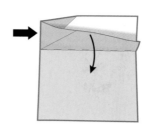

30a. Pull the layer nearest you down, using the horizontal crease as a hinge. Push on the folded edge of the paper to begin flattening the left triangle.

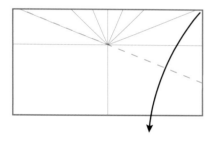

30b. Continue the process until you can flatten the paper to match the illustration in Step 31.

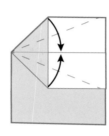

31. Fold the edges of the top triangle in as shown to land on the horizontal edge.

32. Unfold.

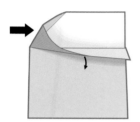

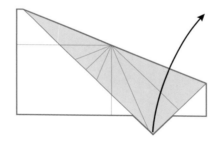

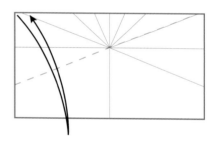

33. Fold along the existing diagonal crease to extend it to both edges of the paper.

34. Unfold.

35. Repeat Steps 33 and 34 on the left side.

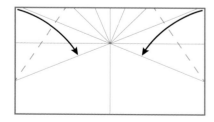

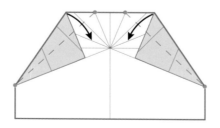

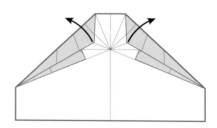

36. Fold the outer edges in to land on the bottom diagonal creases.

37. Fold on the indicated lines, using the highlighted points as your references.

38. Unfold.

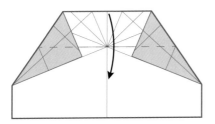

39. Fold the top edge down again using the existing horizontal crease.

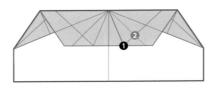

40a. Crease 1 should be a valley crease and crease 2 should be a mountain crease. Follow Steps 40b through 40d to perform a swivel fold using these creases.

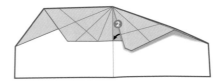

40b. Pull crease 2, aiming to land it on the center crease. The paper should fold along creases 1, 2, and 3 as you do so.

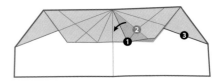

40c. Continue pulling crease 2, aiming to land it on the center crease.

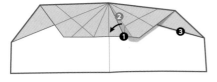

40d. Flatten the paper to match the illustration in Step 41.

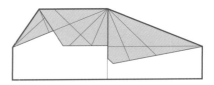

41. Repeat Steps 40a through 40d on the left side.

42. Mountain fold the sections highlighted in green along the existing horizontal crease. Tuck them behind all other layers to lock the layers together.

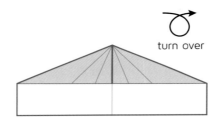

turn over

43. Turn the plane over.

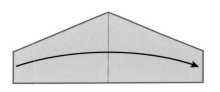

44. Fold the plane in half using its existing center crease.

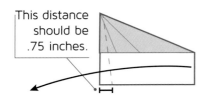

This distance should be .75 inches.

45. Fold the wing on the indicated line.

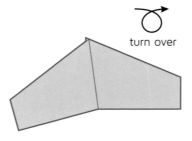

turn over

46. Turn the plane over.

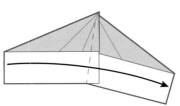

47. Fold the other wing to match the first.

turn over

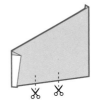

48. Fold a fin on the indicated line. Make sure your crease is parallel to the highlighted edge.

49. Turn the plane over.

50. Fold the other fin to match the first.

51. Hold the two wings in alignment and cut the trailing edge of both wings to form the elevators.

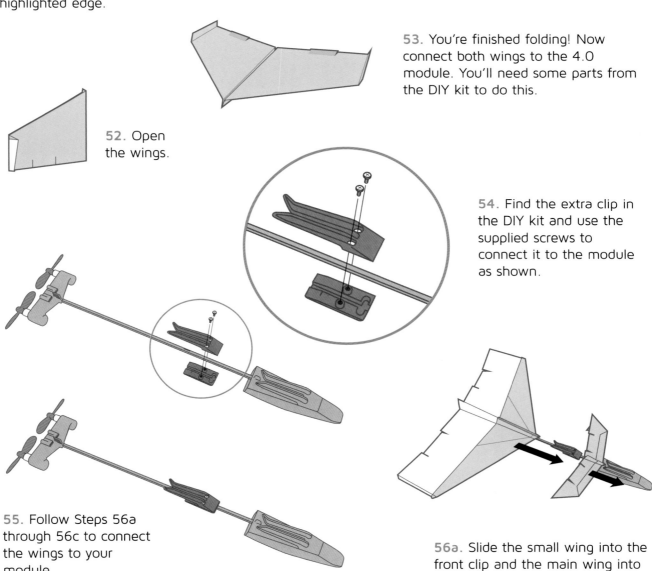

53. You're finished folding! Now connect both wings to the 4.0 module. You'll need some parts from the DIY kit to do this.

52. Open the wings.

54. Find the extra clip in the DIY kit and use the supplied screws to connect it to the module as shown.

55. Follow Steps 56a through 56c to connect the wings to your module.

56a. Slide the small wing into the front clip and the main wing into the rear clip.

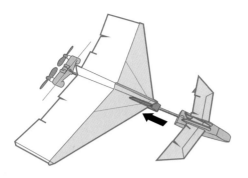

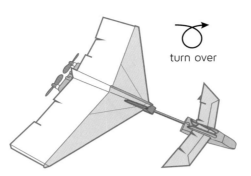

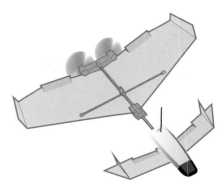

56b. Slide the rear clip and main wing backwards as far as you can (to the red line) until the rear edge of the wing gently meets the screw mounts at the rear of the 4.0 module.

56c. Turn the plane over.

57. Finished!

ADJUST THE FLYING SPEED OF HAMMERHEAD

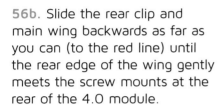

You can adjust the natural flying speed of Hammerhead by sliding the rear wing forward or backward. I'm all about speed, so if you followed the instructions and slide the rear wing all the way back to the screw mounts, your plane is going to fly like a bullet! That said, it can be a lot of fun (and very informative) to experiment by changing the location of the wing. The farther forward you slide it, the slower your plane will fly.

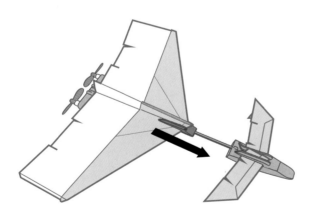

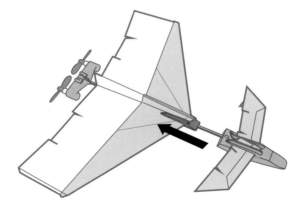

Slide the wing forward to make the plane fly slower.

Slide the wing backward to make the plane fly faster.